THE BETHL
ROYAL HOSI

An Illustrated Hist_⌐

Patricia Allderidge
Archivist and Curator

Left: List of patients in Bethlem, 4 December 1598. (Minutes of the Court of Governors of Bridewell and Bethlem.)

Below and right: Replicas of wooden almsboxes. The originals date from 1676.

Contents

The Bethlem and Maudsley
NHS Trust
1995
ISBN 0 9511782 6 1

1. *Bishopsgate 1247 - 1676*

Bethlem Hospital was founded on 23 October 1247 by Simon Fitzmary, an Alderman and former sheriff of the City of London. Fitzmary's intention was not to found a hospital at all, but a priory which would be a daughter house of the Church of St Mary of Bethlehem. He gave to the Church all the land together with the 'houses, gardens, orchards, fishponds, ditches, and marshes' which he owned in Bishopsgate Street, just outside the City walls, and in due course the Priory of St Mary of Bethlehem was built on the site. The whole area is now covered by Liverpool Street Station.

Plaque on the Great Eastern Hotel, Liverpool Street. (Liverpool Street was called 'Bethlem Street' until 1825).

Little is known about Simon Fitzmary and still less about his motivation, except for his own declared 'special and single minded devotion to the Church of the glorious Virgin Mary at Bethlehem' which is described at some length in the foundation deed. The fact that his own surname means 'son of Mary' may be connected with this special reverence for the Virgin and her church: but it is also known that in 1247 the Bishop of Bethlehem was touring England on a fund-raising mission to restore the fortunes of the mother church in Palestine, and the foundation of this new priory seems to have been one of his most successful coups.

Little is known either about how the priory became a hospital for the sick, but it is already referred to as the Hospital of St Mary of Bethlehem in a document of 1329. The first definite evidence that it was being used to house insane patients dates from 1403, when it contained, besides various other poor and infirm people, '*sex viri menti capti*' (literally, 'six men whose minds had been seized'). Bethlem has had a continuous history of caring for the mentally disordered from this time on, and is probably the oldest such hospital still functioning in Europe, if not in the world. The names 'Bethlem', and the more notorious 'Bedlam' by which it was known for several centuries, are both medieval variants of the original 'Bethlehem'.

Map of the Moorfields area, c. 1559, showing the buildings of 'Bedlame' in Bishopsgate Street. (Reproduced by courtesy of the Museum of London).

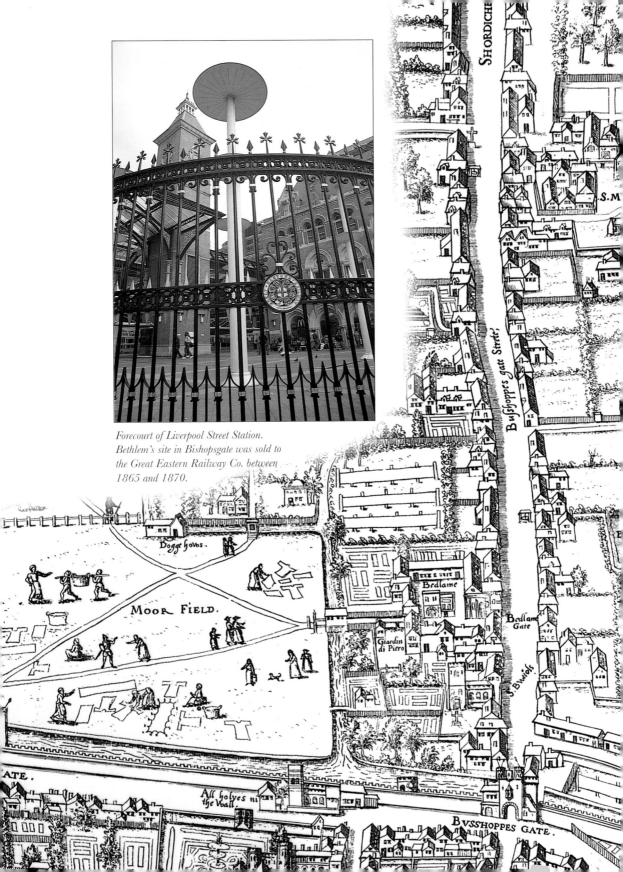

Forecount of Liverpool Street Station. Bethlem's site in Bishopsgate was sold to the Great Eastern Railway Co. between 1865 and 1870.

SHORDICHE

Buſshoppes gate Strete

Doggehows.

MOOR FIELD.

Bedlame

Bedlam Gate

Giardin di Piero

S. Bwiofs

All holyes ni the Voall

BVSSHOPPES GATE.

Portrait of King Henry VIII, attributed to the circle of Hans Holbein, in the Board Room of Bethlem Hospital.

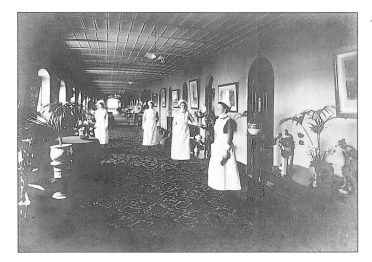

A women's ward in the 1920s.

In 1870 a convalescent establishment was opened at Witley in Surrey. The boys' section of King Edward's School (Bridewell Hospital) had already moved there, and the Bethlem convalescent home was built in the school grounds. The country surroundings and more relaxed regime were popular with both patients and staff, and a ward in the present hospital is named 'Witley' in memory of happy associations with this place.

The chapel in the dome, late 19th century.

Design for the convalescent home at Witley, 1865.

The present Bethlem Hospital in Monks Orchard Road, Beckenham. View from the gate, October 1995.

Queen Mary touring the new hospital, after the official opening on 9 July 1930. The Queen became President of Bridewell and Bethlem in 1941, and Patron of the new joint hospital formed by Bethlem and The Maudsley in 1948.

4.   *Monks Orchard 1930*

The 1920s saw the hospital ready to move once more. The 1815 building, based on a plan conceived in the late 17th century, was by now completely outdated, and the site was restricted by urban development. 'Light, air and space' were needed, as well as 'ultra modern' facilities for both patients and staff. It was decided to rebuild this time in rural surroundings, but within easy reach of London.

In 1924 the governors bought the Monks Orchard Estate, a large country house estate which straddled the Kent/Surrey border and was then mainly in the parish of Addington. Subsequently split between the boroughs of Bromley and Croydon, it has recently been transferred wholly to Bromley. Further complications over the Southwark lease led to the new property being conveyed to the Corporation of London, and then leased back for what still remained of the 999 year term which commenced in 1674.

In design the new hospital was a deliberate break away from the oppressive barracks-like institutions of the previous century, and particularly from the vast county asylums which had come to dominate the psychiatric scene. Planned on the 'villa' system, it originally had four wards, Tyson, Gresham, Fitzmary and Witley, each occupying a separate building with its own kitchen and dining room, and self-contained garden. The total accommodation was for 250 patients. Other independent units included an administration block, a nurses' home, recreation hall, chapel, staff restaurant and kitchen, and 'science and treatment laboratories.'

Aerial view of the hospital at Monks Orchard, taken in 1947 for the 700th anniversary of Bethlem's foundation.

The joint architects were John A Cheston, the surveyor of Bridewell and Bethlem, and Charles E Elcock. Work was begun in 1928, and the new hospital was opened (if not quite finished) in July 1930 by Queen Mary. The buildings are in warm red brick with stone dressings, and are discreetly ornamented in the art deco Egyptian style, best seen in the Administration Unit. The chapel, with its barrel vault flanked by bronze lamps in imitation of oil lamps, and stained glass by William Morris & Co, is especially impressive.

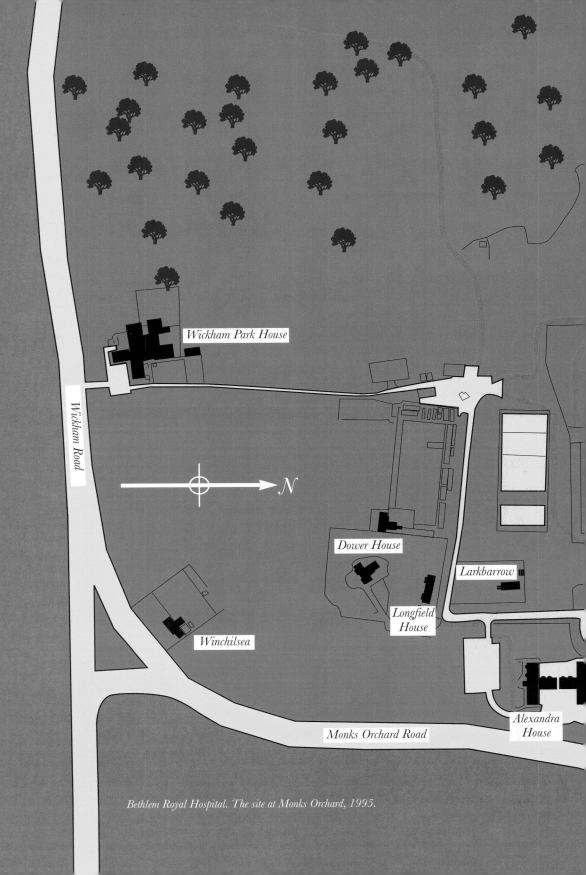

Bethlem Royal Hospital. The site at Monks Orchard, 1995.

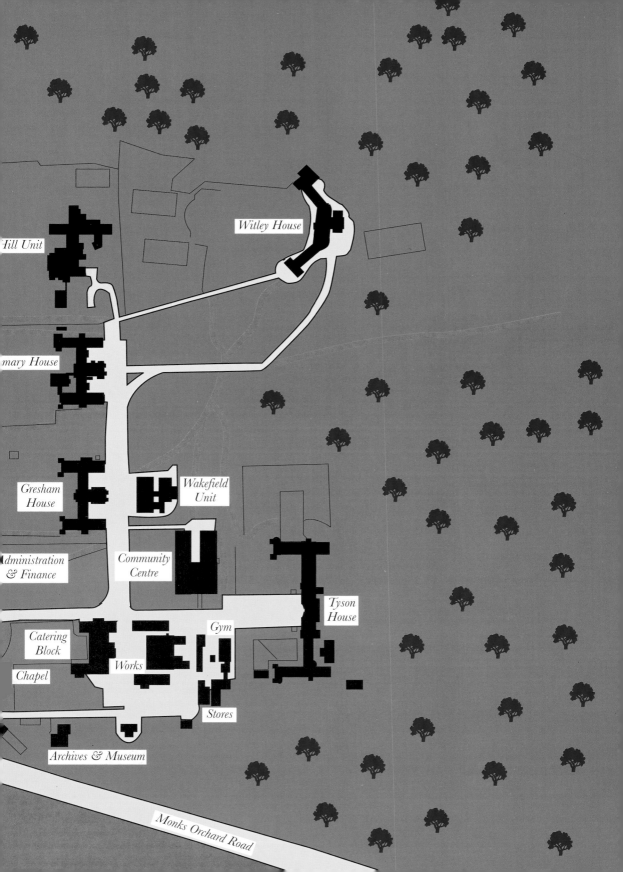

Hill Unit

Witley House

mary House

Gresham
House

Wakefield
Unit

Administration
& Finance

Community
Centre

Tyson
House

Catering
Block

Gym

Chapel

Works

Stores

Archives & Museum

Monks Orchard Road

The Maudsley Hospital in Denmark Hill, London SE5.

Dr Henry Maudsley (born 1835), aged about eighty.

The National Health Service and the Maudsley

In July 1948, under the National Health Service, Bethlem was united with the Maudsley Hospital in Camberwell to form a single postgraduate psychiatric teaching hospital. The name proposed for this new institution, 'The Royal Psychiatric Hospital', was vetoed by the Ministry of Health, and it was called 'The Bethlem Royal Hospital and The Maudsley Hospital'. More recently 'The Maudsley' has been adopted for the whole organisation, but a version of the original name survives in the newly formed Bethlem and Maudsley NHS Trust, and Bethlem as a separate entity retains its own name.

The Maudsley was a London County Council mental hospital, founded early in this century on the initiative of Dr Henry Maudsley, an eminent psychiatrist whose reputation and influence had been achieved mainly through his writings. Maudsley gave £30,000 to the Council, covering half the cost of building the hospital. He also, in collaboration with Sir Frederick Mott, the pathologist to the LCC Asylums, laid down strict conditions which were closely followed: it was to be small; to be for early and acute cases only; to have research facilities; to become a medical school of the University of London; and to be in a central position within three to four miles of Trafalgar Square.

The Institute of Psychiatry. The Institute was housed in the Maudsley Hospital until 1967, when it moved into this new building on an adjacent site.

Intentionally as unlike as possible to the Victorian asylums, The Maudsley was modelled on German university psychiatric clinics such as Kraepelin's clinic at Munich. After serving as a military hospital treating shellshock cases during the 1914-18 war, it finally opened under LCC control in 1923, and rapidly gained an international reputation for teaching and research. In 1948 its medical school, renamed the Institute of Psychiatry, became a constituent body of the British Postgraduate Medical Federation within the University of London.

Since there was only room in London for one psychiatric teaching hospital under the NHS, and The Maudsley was clearly destined to be it, Bethlem had little option but to join forces. (It had itself been recognised as a medical school of the University of London since 1924, but had lost this status in 1946.) The fact that Bethlem was by now adequately endowed and The Maudsley, under the LCC, was not, made this an obvious marriage of convenience.

5. *Charity and Endowments*

For most of its history, Bethlem has been a charitable institution for the poor. In the medieval period support could be literally hand-to-mouth, with food being delivered direct to the hospital at the charge of benevolent citizens. As late as 1633 it is recorded that every Monday the Lord Mayor sent in '6 penny household loaves .... Of beefe 2 Stone at the Least .... and a pott of pottage made with halfe a pecke of oatemeale'. The two Sheriffs contributed the same amount on Wednesdays and Thursdays.

Cash donations were still more important, and played a large part in the governors' failure to end the unedifying practice of opening the hospital to the public sooner than they did. The money given by visitors to 'the Poor's Box' went a long way towards paying the bills. One event specially designed to encourage charitable giving was the annual Spital Sermon, preached at Easter before the Mayor and Aldermen during the 17th and 18th centuries to invoke patronage for all the five Royal Hospitals.

18th century almsbox inscribed: 'Pray Remember the Poor Lunaticks and Put Your Charity into this Box With Your Own Hand'.

One of Bethlem's best known tenants on the Piccadilly estate.

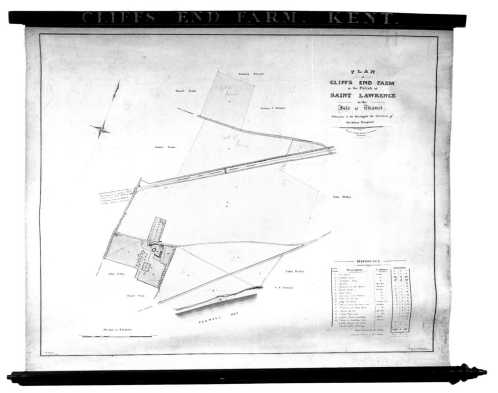

Estate plan of Cliffs End Farm near Ramsgate, 1853. Bequeathed to Bethlem in 1702, this is the only farm still owned by the hospital.

Eventually the most important source of income came to be the permanent endowment which grew up over the centuries through donations and bequests, particularly bequests of property. The latter included several farms in Kent, and a large agricultural estate in Lincolnshire. Apart from the original site in Bishopsgate, the oldest and most substantial of Bethlem's London properties was at Charing Cross. Owned by the hospital since before 1403, this was exchanged in 1830 for an estate of equal value in Piccadilly, and is now part of Trafalgar Square.

Bethlem was able to keep its endowments under the provisions for teaching hospitals within the National Health Service, though sharing them equally with The Maudsley. The Board of Governors of the new joint hospital became trustees of these funds, succeeded in 1982 by a Special Health Authority, and in 1994 by the Bethlem and Maudsley NHS Trust. While day-to-day funding has since 1948 come from the Exchequer, Bethlem's historic possessions have been able to provide additional resources for many important projects, and particularly for research.

6. *Patients*

Bethlem has always been a 'real' hospital, in the sense that patients were admitted in order to be cured, but in its early days, those who did not recover might stay for many years. The first full list of patients (illustrated inside front cover), dating from 1598, includes one woman who had been in the hospital for twenty-five years, but ten of the twenty-one inmates had been in for a year or less. In the next century it became the practice to discharge those who seemed unlikely to recover, and this developed into a rule that no patient should remain for longer than twelve months.

As the 1598 list already shows, patients were admitted from all over the country. This reflects the fact that for several centuries, Bethlem was the only public institution for the mentally disordered. (The main local alternatives which were to grow up later were the private madhouses, which flourished from the 18th century on, and the county asylums of the 19th century.)

For most of its history, Bethlem's patients have come from the ranks of the very poor, and with a few notable exceptions, little is known of most of them beyond their names and places of origin, recorded in admission registers which date back to 1683. Even the more detailed casebooks of the 19th century tell us relatively little of these people outside their brief passage through the hospital, though a remarkable set of photographs taken in the 1850s adds an extra and moving dimension to the record.

Daniel, Oliver Cromwell's porter, who was a patient in Bethlem for some years after his admission in 1656.

A change in social status took place in the mid 19th century. It was decided to exclude pauper patients, who could now be cared for in the new county asylums, and give preference to the poor of the middle classes. In 1882 the first handful of paying patients were admitted , and inevitably the numbers crept up (though the 'free list' was never wholly abandoned). By the time the new hospital opened in 1930, the prospectus was referring to 'accommodation for 141 ladies and 109 gentlemen, each of whom must be of suitable educational status'.

Under the NHS, in conjunction with The Maudsley, Bethlem became part of a system based largely on specialist units and treatments, and clinical considerations took over from social and financial circumstances as the main criteria for admission. The new Trust has now taken responsibility for mental healthcare in the Croydon area, introducing for the first time (for Bethlem though not for The Maudsley) a service for the local community.

These two photographs show the same patient, the first while suffering from 'puerperal mania', the second during convalescence. From a series taken in the 1850s.

Long stay patients: the Criminal Department and the 'Incurables'.

Although Bethlem was a hospital for curable cases, there were two exceptions to this rule. In the 18th century provision was made for a limited number of 'incurable' patients, fifty each of men and women, but only for those who had already been discharged uncured and for whom no care could be provided by their families or friends. Happily some did eventually recover, but most remained until they died, and patients who were discharged 'fit' for the incurable department generally had to be put on a waiting list for a vacancy. The numbers were gradually reduced in the 19th century, and admissions to this department ended in 1919.

In the 19th century, the Criminal Department also housed long stay patients. This was actually the first State Criminal Lunatic Asylum, built and maintained at government expense and controlled by the Home Office, but physically attached to Bethlem and run by the hospital on a day-to-day basis. An Act of Parliament of 1800 had provided that people charged with criminal offences who were found to be insane, should be ordered by the courts to be detained 'until His Majesty's Pleasure shall be known.' Two wings at Bethlem were opened in 1816 for this category of patient, to be replaced in 1864 by a completely new institution at Broadmoor in Berkshire. Some of Bethlem's most famous patients were confined in the Criminal Department, including the painter Richard Dadd; Jonathan Martin, who set fire to York Minster; and Edward Oxford, who fired two pistols at Queen Victoria.

In 1985 forensic psychiatry returned to Bethlem with the opening of the Denis Hill Unit, a South East Thames Regional Medium Secure Unit. This was built to house patients requiring treatment within a secure environment, but not the very high security of the Special Hospitals such as Broadmoor.

Margaret Nicholson, a patient in Bethlem from 1786-1828, admitted at the request of King George III after she had attempted to stab him and had been found to be insane.

Edward Oxford firing at Queen Victoria in 1840. He was acquitted on grounds of insanity and confined in the Criminal Department for twenty four years, though consistently reported by the physicians to be sane.

Poem and drawing by James Hadfield, whose assassination attempt on King George III in 1800 led to the first criminal lunacy legislation.

The painter Richard Dadd, a patient in the Criminal Department from 1844-1864, at work on his fairy painting 'Contradiction. Oberon and Titania' in the 1850s.

7. Medical and Nursing Staff

This scene from 'A Rake's Progress' shows (presumably) a keeper removing the Rake's leg irons. The man standing behind may be the physician or apothecary.

It is not clear precisely who looked after the patients during the hospital's earliest days. The religious order attached to the priory had been disbanded by the time insane patients first came into residence, but a secular 'confraternity' of St Mary of Bethlehem survived and may have played some part in their care. By the mid 17th century attendants were being employed, and in 1643 there is a reference to 'lodgings for servants to take care of the lunatics'.

Until the 19th century male attendants were generally called 'basketmen', a name shrouded in mystery. Possibly it referred to some early practice of collecting food in baskets for the patients, or possibly to the symbol of a basket of bread which appears in Bethlem's coat of arms. They were also called 'keepers'. This name changed to 'attendants' in 1843, and to 'male nurses' after the first world war. Female attendants, earlier known as 'gallery maids', were called 'nurses' by 1893, soon after they had started wearing a uniform similar to nurses' uniforms in general hospitals.

Mrs Emma Dunn, Matron of Bethlem 1854-1869.

Bethlem already had a Matron by 1630, though at this time the role was taken by the Porter's wife, without additional salary. The Matron supervised the work of all the female servants, and the care of the female patients, and the post gradually increased in responsibility. By the 19th century the Matron had considerable authority on 'the female side', though there was also a Head Attendant for the male side. In recent times the title of the principal nursing post has varied, including Superintendent of Nursing, Chief Nursing Officer, and Chief Nursing Adviser.

The appointment of a regular physician seems to date properly from 1634. (The previous Keeper or Master had actually been a physician, but like most occupants of this post he was largely absent.) From 1728 to 1853, four generations of the Monro family held the post of Physician to Bethlem Hospital. It did not become a full time or resident post until the 1850s, and before this time the Apothecary was the only resident medical officer.

By the late 19th century there were two Assistant Medical Officers on the permanent staff, and by 1948 the Physician Superintendent was still assisted only by three senior medical officers. The Maudsley style staffing of the new joint hospital must have induced some culture shock. It included a Professor of Psychiatry, Assistant Clinical Director, five full and nine part time Senior and six full and five part time Junior Physicians, and fifteen Registrars.

Staff fancy dress ball, January 1907. Sister Simpson as 'Bethlem Hospital'.

Attendants and brothers Edward and Alfred Cantle, founder members of the hospital band, c. 1900. Edward Cantle's daughter and son also joined the nursing staff.

A staff line up during a 'private and informal' visit by the Duke of Connaught (centre), a governor of the hospital, in 1924.

8. *Treatment*

Contrary to popular belief, mental disorder has been regarded as potentially curable throughout the hospital's history. Whether many of the 'cures' in vogue at different times over the past centuries have played much part in the patients' recovery, is another question. Nevertheless a proportion (perhaps just over 30% in the 18th century) did recover, though some might relapse later and be readmitted.

In the absence of *effective* treatments, most of which have been developed in the present century, physical restraint featured prominently in Bethlem's regime, but this was never the whole story. Both medical and psychological methods of treatment have long been in use. Medicines have probably always been administered, and in 1700 a fund was set up to provide 'Phisick' for discharged patients to prevent their relapse. However, under the Monro family's long reign as physicians medication made little progress. Their practice, handed down from father to son, can be summarised as 'purges, vomits, and bloodletting' - standard treatment in the early 18th century, but distinctly outmoded by the mid 19th.

Cold and warm bathing, introduced in the 1680s, seems more likely to have benefited the patients, particularly 'in the Heat of the Weather...to cool and wash them'. Occupation, and distraction from false, deluded or melancholy thoughts, was also considered important. By 1765, for example, it was one of the matron's duties to make sure that the women patients who were 'low spirited or inclinable to be mopish' should get up and not be allowed to slink back to bed, and to employ those who were capable at needlework. In the 19th century occupation and entertainments multiplied. Dances were held in Bethlem as early as the 1840s, outings and excursions took place, and many other activities were introduced.

Huge advances in scientific knowledge, particularly in the understanding of brain function and the development of effective drugs for many conditions, together with a wide range of techniques based on psychotherapy, have revolutionised treatments in the second half of the 20th century.

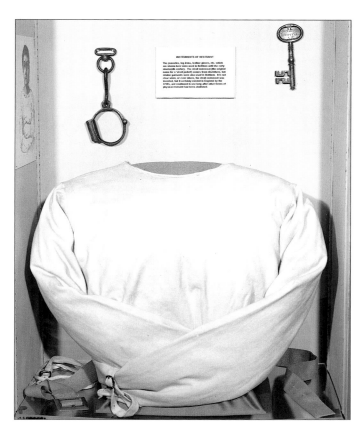

Instruments of restraint on show in the museum: iron manacle and strait waistcoat. The key, dating from the late 18th or early 19th century, is inscribed 'Bethlem Hospital №15'.

Croquet: one of the many occupations and amusements introduced in the second half of the 19th century.

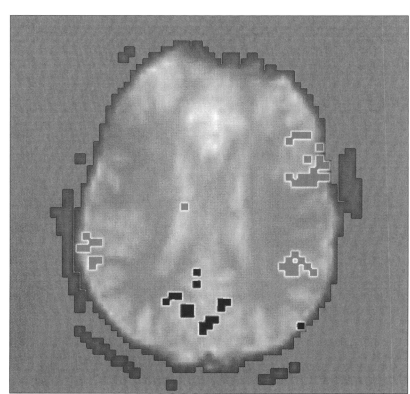

A functional magnetic resonance image (MRI), showing areas of the brain activated during verbal fluency tests which are being developed for use in understanding depression. (Reproduced by courtesy of the Depression IRG, Institute of Psychiatry.)

9. *The Hospital Today*

The Bethlem and Maudsley NHS Trust comprises the Maudsley Hospital, Bethlem Royal Hospital, Croydon Mental Health Services (currently based at Warlingham Park Hospital, Surrey), and a range of community-based services. Through continuing close links with the Institute of Psychiatry, it forms a world renowned centre for treatment, research and training in psychiatry and mental health.

It is only possible to mention a few of the specialist services within the joint organisation. Amongst those based at Bethlem are the Mother and Baby Unit, Eating Disorders Unit, Drug Treatment and Rehabilitation Units, Child and Adolescent Units, and the Denis Hill (Forensic Psychiatry) Unit. Psychosis, neurosis, depression, Alzheimer's disease, traumatic stress disorder, epilepsy, drug and alcohol addiction, autism, and behaviour disorders, are just some of the fields in which close collaboration between clinical and research teams helps to develop and evaluate treatments, and to pioneer new ones. The acquisition of one of the most advanced Magnetic Resonance scanners has made The Maudsley a world centre in the development of sophisticated brain imaging techniques. These are already providing new understanding of disorders such as schizophrenia, epilepsy, stroke and dementia.

Staff canteen →
All wards(except HLH) →
O. T. department →
Gymnasium →
Community Centre →
Swimming pool →
Path. laboratory →
Pharmacy →
X-ray / E. C. T. →
Linen room →
Psychology →
Sports grounds →

10. The Art and History Collections

Over the centuries Bethlem has accumulated an exceptionally rich archive of written and pictorial records, which continues to grow. In 1967 the Board of Governors set up an archives department to ensure that this invaluable source material would be preserved for the future and be accessible for historical research.

A new building was put up, to house both the archives and a small museum in which to exhibit the hospital's collection of historical objects and works of art. The latter include many fine watercolours by Bethlem's most famous patient, the 19th century painter Richard Dadd. The museum has been open to the public since 1970. It now also holds the Guttmann-Maclay picture collection (formerly at the Institute of Psychiatry), comprising paintings and drawings by artists who have suffered from mental disorder. The museum collections also continue to grow.

Together the art and history collections offer unique insights into the historical and cultural background against which this ancient hospital now meets the challenges of late 20th century psychiatry.

Richard Dadd, 'Portrait of Sir Thomas Phillips in Arab Costume'. (Acquired with grants from the MGC/V&A Purchase Grant Fund, the National Art Collections Fund, and the Pilgrim Trust).

Louis Wain, Cat Pattern.

Books and documents from the archives.

Chronology

1247 23 October. The Priory of St Mary of Bethlehem, Bishopsgate, is founded by Simon Fitzmary.

1329 First surviving reference to the priory as a 'hospice' or 'hospital'.

1346 The hospital appeals to the City of London for protection and patronage, and has links with the City from this time on.

1403 An inquisition into malpractices at the hospital finds six insane men in residence there. First reference to Bethlem's use as a hospital for the insane.

1547 January. Letters patent of Henry VIII, confirming an agreement of the previous December, grant the 'custody order and government' of the hospital to the City of London.

1553 Foundation of Bridewell Hospital by Edward VI.

1557 Bridewell and Bethlem are placed under a joint administration.

1598 The first complete list of patients is recorded in the governors' minutes.

1634 The first visiting physician is appointed.

1676 Bethlem moves to a new building at Moorfields, the first custom-built hospital for the insane in the country.

1683 Admission registers begin.

1723/33

      Two wings are added to the building, for incurable patients.

1733 Edward Barkham bequeaths an estate in Lincolnshire to support the incurable department.

1770 Indiscriminate visiting by the public is ended by order of the governors.

1815 First report of the Parliamentary Committee appointed to consider 'the better regulation of madhouses in England' reveals abuses and ill treatment at Bethlem and elsewhere.

1815 The hospital moves to a new building at St George's Fields, Southwark.

1816 The first State Criminal Lunatic Asylum is opened at Bethlem, under the control of the Home Office.

1838 Building extensions are begun which almost double the accommodation.

1846 The dome is completed.

1852 The first resident Physician Superintendent is appointed, and a major programme of reform is begun.

1853 The Lunacy Commissioners are empowered to make regular inspections of the hospital.

1857 Pauper patients are no longer admitted from this time.

1863/64

      Criminal patients are transferred to Broadmoor, and the 'criminal wings' demolished.

1870 A convalescent establishment is opened at Witley in Surrey.

1882 Permission is granted by the Charity Commissioners for the first paying patients to be admitted.

1907 Dr Henry Maudsley offers £30,000 to the LCC for the establishment of a hospital for early and acute cases of mental illness.

1915 The Maudsley Hospital buildings are completed in Denmark Hill, and used as a military hospital.

1919 Bethlem opens an outpatients department, the 'Hospital for Nervous Diseases', at 52 Lambeth Road.

1923 The Maudsley Hospital is opened as an LCC mental hospital.

1924 Both Bethlem and The Maudsley are admitted as Medical Schools of the University of London.

1925 The Monks Orchard Estate is bought by the governors of Bethlem.

1930 The hospital moves to Monks Orchard.

1948 July. Introduction of the National Health Service. The Bethlem Royal Hospital and The Maudsley Hospital are merged to form a postgraduate psychiatric teaching hospital.

1982 The Bethlem Royal Hospital and The Maudsley Hospital Special Health Authority replaces the Board of Governors.

1994 The Bethlem and Maudsley NHS Trust is established.

1995 The Trust takes over responsibility for Croydon Mental Health Services, giving Bethlem a local commitment for the first time.